Mathematics through discovery and practice

"Mathematics is a discovery of relationships and the expression of the relationship in symbolic (or abstract) form . . . . . .

Practice is necessary to fix a concept, once it is understood. Therefore practice should follow, not precede, discovery".

(Curriculum Bulletin No. I of the Schools Council.)

Children make their own discoveries about number, if they have suitable experiences, especially in real life situations. Numbers are not met in isolation from language or experience.

Practice in the four rules of Arithmetic is presented in these four carefully graded books of the Ladybird Basic Arithmetic Series:-

Book I covers the 100 basic facts of addition

Book 2 covers the 100 basic facts of subtraction

Book 3 covers the 100 basic facts of multiplication

Book 4 covers the 90 basic facts of division

Each of these 390 essential number combinations is linked with an attractive illustration which offers the maximum help for happy learning.

See also Books 1 - 4 in the Ladybird "Words for Number" Series

Book 2

THE LADYBIRD
BASIC ARITHMETIC SERIES

Subtraction made easy

by W. MURRAY
(Author of the Ladybird Key Words Reading Scheme)

Ladybird Books Ltd Loughborough

1 2 3 4 5 6 7

Write your answers in your exercise book

From 3 take 1

(Answer 2)

From 4 take 2

From 2 take 1

From 3 take 2

4

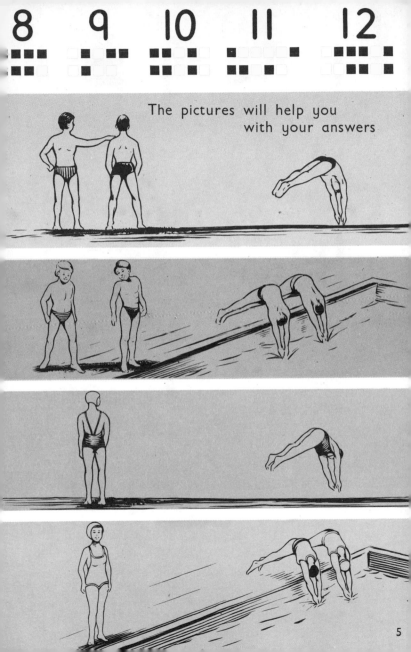

The pictures will help you
with your answers

$$4 - 1 =$$

$$4 - 3 =$$

$$5 - 1 =$$

$$5 - 2 =$$

$$5 - 3 =$$

$$5 - 4 =$$

$$1 - 1 =$$

$$6 - 1 =$$

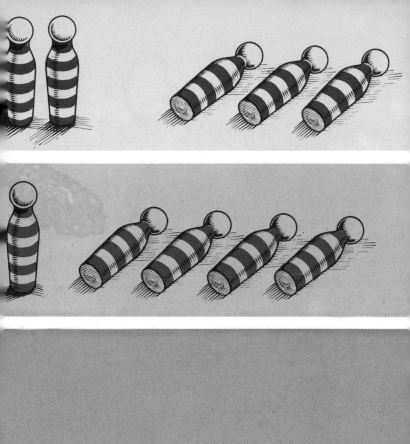

9

$$1 - 0 =$$

$$2 - 0 =$$

$$2 - 2 =$$

$$6 - 3 =$$

$$3 - 0 =$$

$$3 - 3 =$$

$$5 - 0 =$$

$$6 - 2 =$$

$$7 - 1 =$$

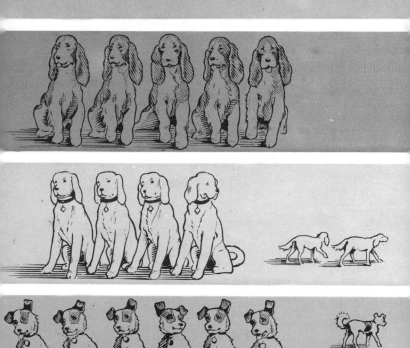

$$6 - 0 =$$

$$6 - 4 =$$

$$4 - 4 =$$

$$7 - 2 =$$

$$8 - 1 =$$

$$4 - 0 =$$

$$5 - 5 =$$

$$6 - 5 =$$

$$7 - 3 =$$

$$8 - 2 =$$

17

$$7 - 0 =$$

$$7 - 4 =$$

$$6 - 6 =$$

$$7 - 5 =$$

$$8 - 3 =$$

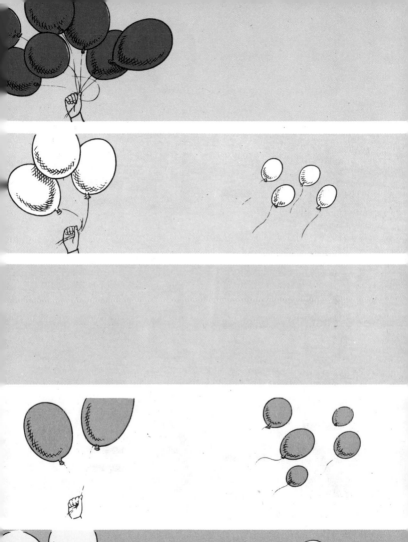

$$8 - 0 =$$

$$8 - 4 =$$

$$8 - 5 =$$

$$7 - 6 =$$

$$7 - 7 =$$

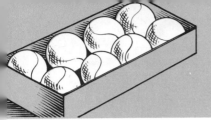

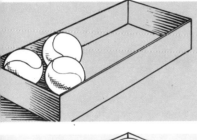

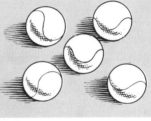

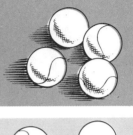

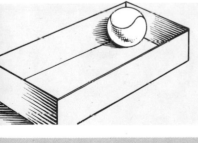

$$9 - 0 =$$

$$9 - 4 =$$

$$8 - 6 =$$

$$0 - 0 =$$

$$9 - 1 =$$

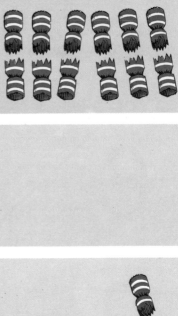

23

$$9 - 3 =$$

$$8 - 7 =$$

$$9 - 2 =$$

$$8 - 8 =$$

$$9 - 8 =$$

25

$9 - 5 =$

$10 - 1 =$

$9 - 6 =$

$9 - 9 =$

$10 - 5 =$

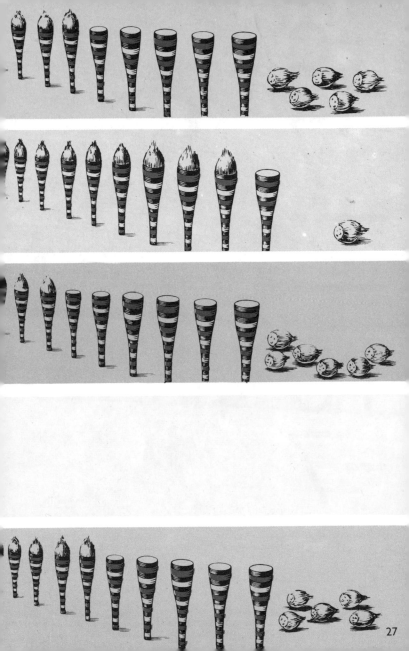

27

$$\begin{array}{r} 9 \\ -7 \\ \hline \\ \hline \end{array}$$

from nine

take seven

$$\begin{array}{r} 10 \\ -7 \\ \hline \\ \hline \end{array}$$

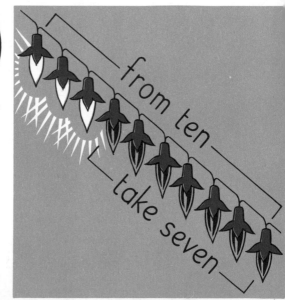

from ten

take seven

28

$$\begin{array}{r} 10 \\ -2 \\ \hline \\ \hline \end{array}$$

$$\begin{array}{r} 10 \\ -6 \\ \hline \\ \hline \end{array}$$

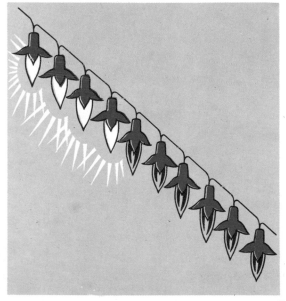

$$\begin{array}{r} 10 \\ -4 \\ \hline \\ \hline \end{array}$$

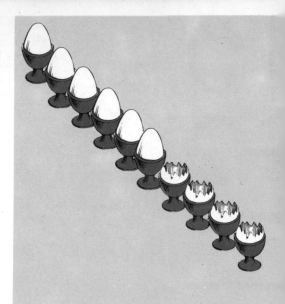

$$\begin{array}{r} 12 \\ -6 \\ \hline \\ \hline \end{array}$$

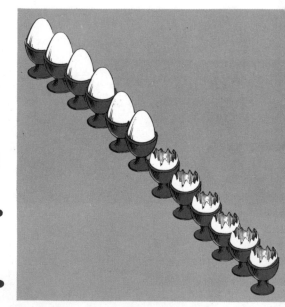

10
-8

1

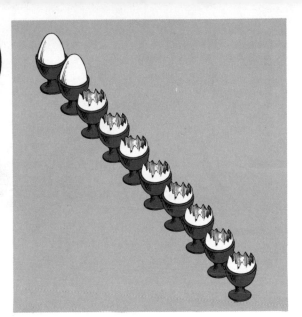

10
-3

7

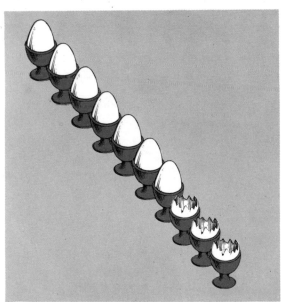

$$\begin{array}{r} 11 \\ -2 \\ \hline \end{array}$$

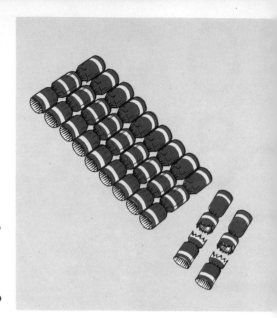

$$\begin{array}{r} 10 \\ -9 \\ \hline \end{array}$$

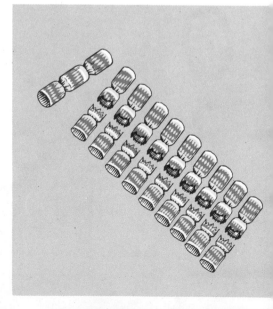

32

| |
3

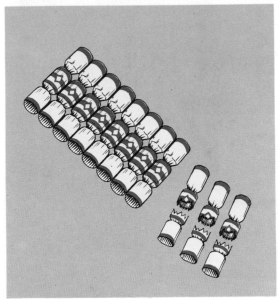

| |
6

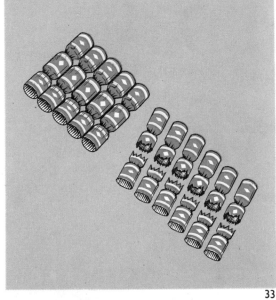

33

$$\begin{array}{r} 11 \\ -7 \\ \hline \end{array}$$

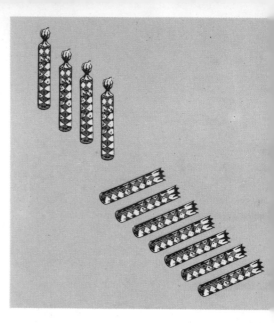

$$\begin{array}{r} 12 \\ -8 \\ \hline \end{array}$$

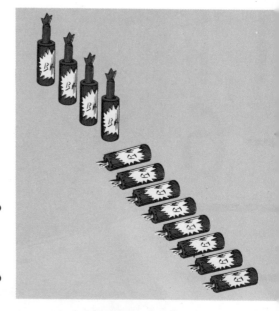

34

11

4

11

11

12

9

11

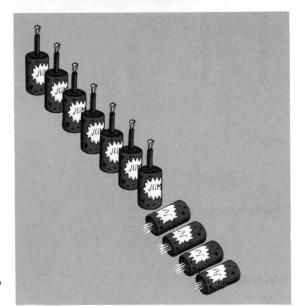

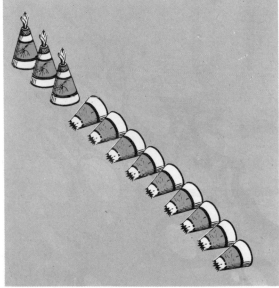

$$11 - 5$$

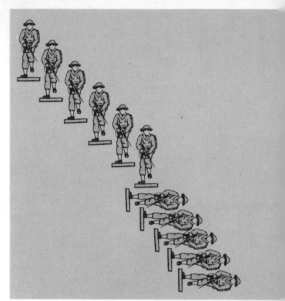

$$11 - 8$$

12
4

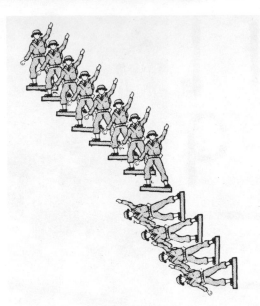

14
7

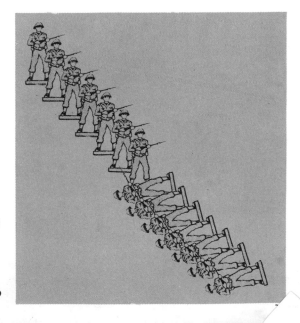

11
−9
‖‖

12
−3
‖

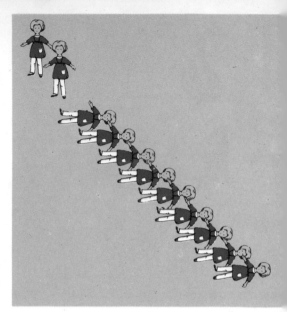

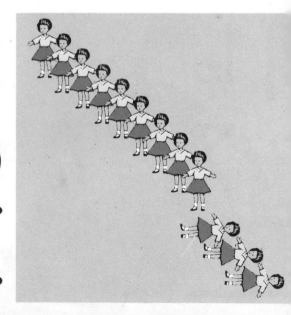

2
5

1
1

1
6
8

1

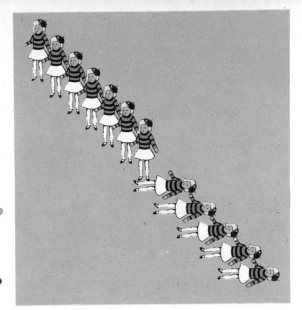

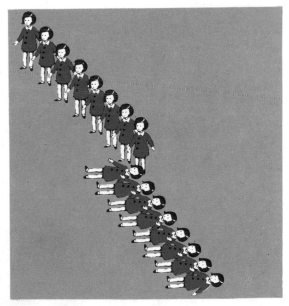

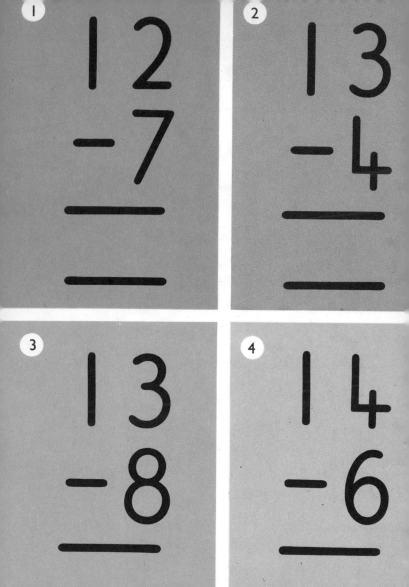

1.
$$
\begin{array}{r}
12 \\
-7 \\
\hline
\\
\hline
\end{array}
$$

2.
$$
\begin{array}{r}
13 \\
-4 \\
\hline
\\
\hline
\end{array}
$$

3.
$$
\begin{array}{r}
13 \\
-8 \\
\hline
\\
\hline
\end{array}
$$

4.
$$
\begin{array}{r}
14 \\
-6 \\
\hline
\\
\hline
\end{array}
$$

1

$$\begin{array}{r} 13 \\ -\ 6 \\ \hline \\ \hline \end{array}$$

2

$$\begin{array}{r} 18 \\ -\ 9 \\ \hline \\ \hline \end{array}$$

3

$$\begin{array}{r} 15 \\ -\ 8 \\ \hline \\ \hline \end{array}$$

4

$$\begin{array}{r} 14 \\ -\ 8 \\ \hline \\ \hline \end{array}$$

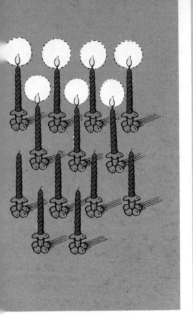

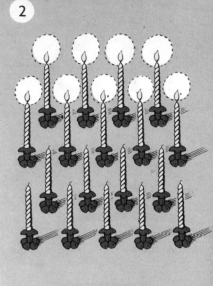

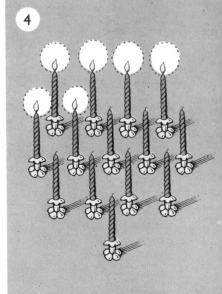

1

$$\begin{array}{r} 15 \\ -7 \\ \hline \\ \hline \end{array}$$

2

$$\begin{array}{r} 14 \\ -9 \\ \hline \\ \hline \end{array}$$

3

$$\begin{array}{r} 13 \\ -9 \\ \hline \\ \hline \end{array}$$

4

$$\begin{array}{r} 14 \\ -5 \\ \hline \\ \hline \end{array}$$

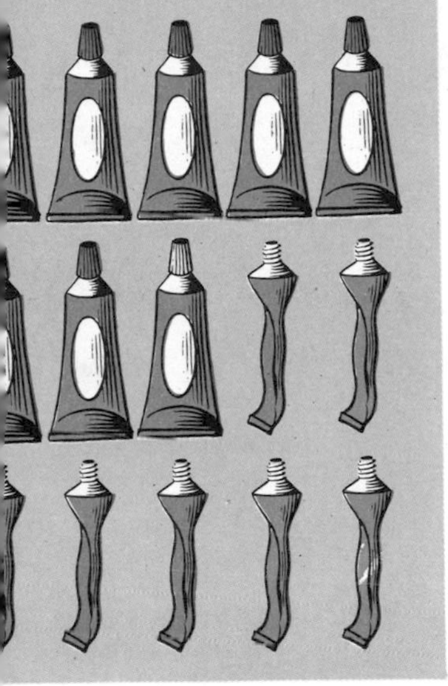

2

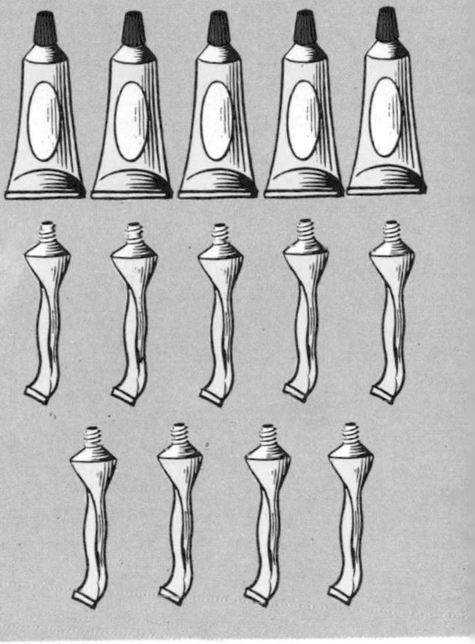

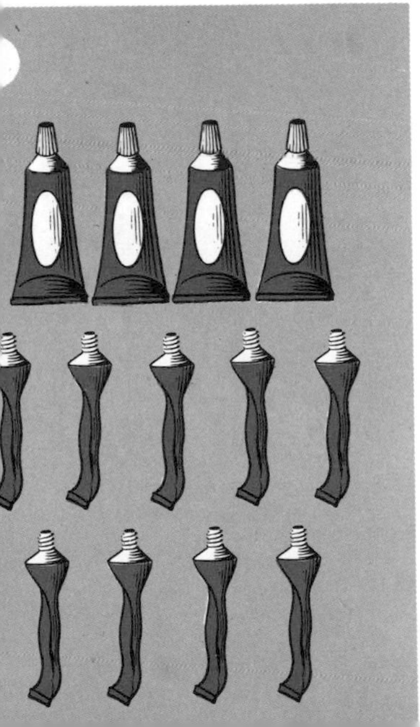

4

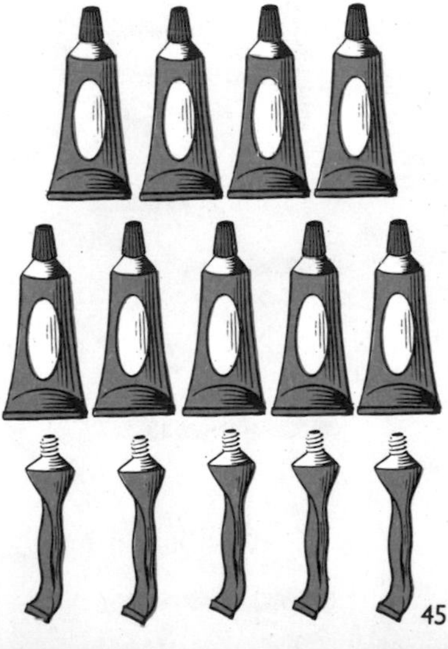

$$\begin{array}{r} 13 \\ -\ 5 \\ \hline \\ \hline \end{array}$$

$$\begin{array}{r} 15 \\ -\ 6 \\ \hline \\ \hline \end{array}$$

$$\begin{array}{r} 16 \\ -\ 7 \\ \hline \\ \hline \end{array}$$

$$\begin{array}{r} 15 \\ -\ 9 \\ \hline \\ \hline \end{array}$$

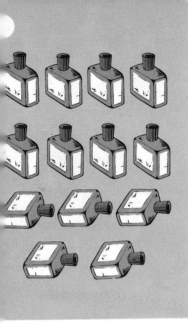

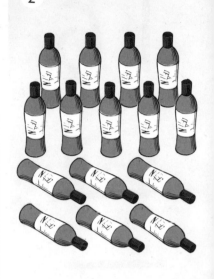

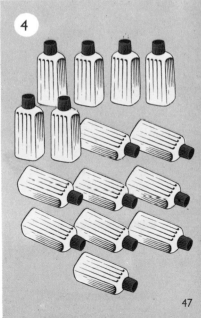

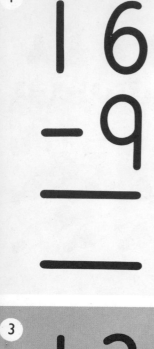

1.
$$16 - 9 = $$

2.
$$17 - = $$

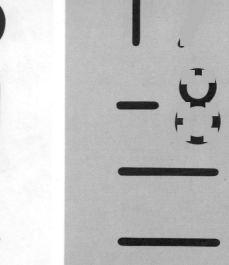

3.
$$13 - 7 = $$

4.
$$17 - = $$

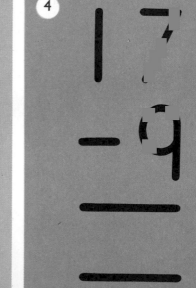

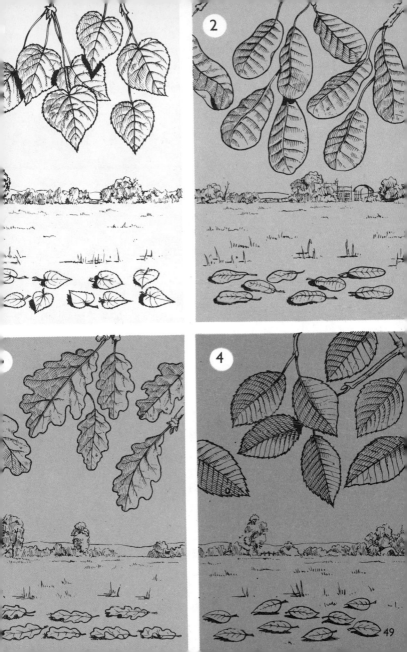

49

TEN TESTS OF TEN SUMS EACH
presenting the 100 basic facts of subtraction

Test 1

$3 - 1 =$	$4 - 2 =$	$2 - 1 =$	$3 - 2 =$	$4 - 1$
$4 - 3 =$	$5 - 1 =$	$5 - 2 =$	$5 - 3 =$	$5 - 4$

Test 2

$1 - 1 =$	$6 - 1 =$	$1 - 0 =$	$2 - 0 =$	$2 - 2 =$
$6 - 3 =$	$3 - 0 =$	$3 - 3 =$	$5 - 0 =$	$6 - 2 =$

Test 3

$7 - 1 =$	$6 - 0 =$	$6 - 4 =$	$4 - 4 =$	$7 - 2 =$
$8 - 1 =$	$4 - 0 =$	$5 - 5 =$	$6 - 5 =$	$7 - 3 =$

Test 4

$8 - 2 =$	$7 - 0 =$	$7 - 4 =$	$6 - 6 =$	$7 - 5 =$
$8 - 3 =$	$8 - 0 =$	$8 - 4 =$	$8 - 5 =$	$7 - 6 =$

Test 5

$7 - 7 =$	$9 - 0 =$	$9 - 4 =$	$8 - 6 =$	$0 - 0 =$
$9 - 1 =$	$9 - 3 =$	$8 - 7 =$	$9 - 2 =$	$8 - 8 =$

Test 6

$9-8=$	$9-5=$	$10-1=$	$9-6=$	$9-9=$
$10-5=$	$\begin{array}{r}9\\-7\\\hline\end{array}$	$\begin{array}{r}10\\-7\\\hline\end{array}$	$\begin{array}{r}10\\-2\\\hline\end{array}$	$\begin{array}{r}10\\-6\\\hline\end{array}$

Test 7

$\begin{array}{r}10\\-4\\\hline\end{array}$	$\begin{array}{r}12\\-6\\\hline\end{array}$	$\begin{array}{r}10\\-8\\\hline\end{array}$	$\begin{array}{r}10\\-3\\\hline\end{array}$	$\begin{array}{r}11\\-2\\\hline\end{array}$
$\begin{array}{r}10\\-9\\\hline\end{array}$	$\begin{array}{r}11\\-3\\\hline\end{array}$	$\begin{array}{r}11\\-6\\\hline\end{array}$	$\begin{array}{r}11\\-7\\\hline\end{array}$	$\begin{array}{r}12\\-8\\\hline\end{array}$

Test 8

$\begin{array}{r}11\\-4\\\hline\end{array}$	$\begin{array}{r}12\\-9\\\hline\end{array}$	$\begin{array}{r}11\\-5\\\hline\end{array}$	$\begin{array}{r}11\\-8\\\hline\end{array}$	$\begin{array}{r}12\\-4\\\hline\end{array}$
$\begin{array}{r}14\\-7\\\hline\end{array}$	$\begin{array}{r}11\\-9\\\hline\end{array}$	$\begin{array}{r}12\\-3\\\hline\end{array}$	$\begin{array}{r}12\\-5\\\hline\end{array}$	$\begin{array}{r}16\\-8\\\hline\end{array}$

Test 9

$\begin{array}{r}12\\-7\\\hline\end{array}$	$\begin{array}{r}13\\-4\\\hline\end{array}$	$\begin{array}{r}13\\-8\\\hline\end{array}$	$\begin{array}{r}14\\-6\\\hline\end{array}$	$\begin{array}{r}13\\-6\\\hline\end{array}$
$\begin{array}{r}18\\-9\\\hline\end{array}$	$\begin{array}{r}15\\-8\\\hline\end{array}$	$\begin{array}{r}14\\-8\\\hline\end{array}$	$\begin{array}{r}15\\-7\\\hline\end{array}$	$\begin{array}{r}14\\-9\\\hline\end{array}$

Test 10

$\begin{array}{r}13\\-9\\\hline\end{array}$	$\begin{array}{r}14\\-5\\\hline\end{array}$	$\begin{array}{r}13\\-5\\\hline\end{array}$	$\begin{array}{r}15\\-6\\\hline\end{array}$	$\begin{array}{r}16\\-7\\\hline\end{array}$
$\begin{array}{r}15\\-9\\\hline\end{array}$	$\begin{array}{r}16\\-9\\\hline\end{array}$	$\begin{array}{r}17\\-8\\\hline\end{array}$	$\begin{array}{r}13\\-7\\\hline\end{array}$	$\begin{array}{r}17\\-9\\\hline\end{array}$

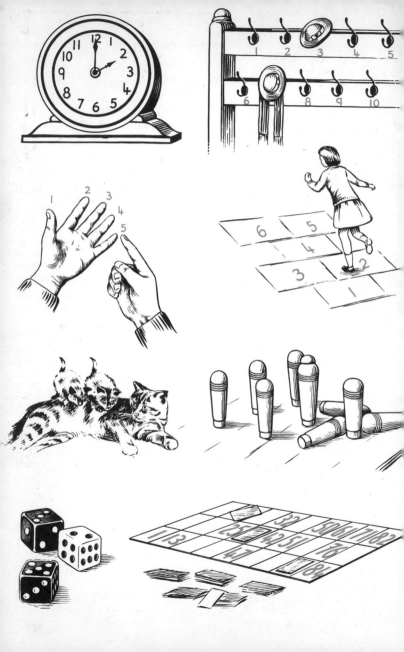